Grade 2 Math

D1209361

Contents

Number the train cars from 1 to 10. The first one is done for you.

Match the word to the number. The first one is done for you.

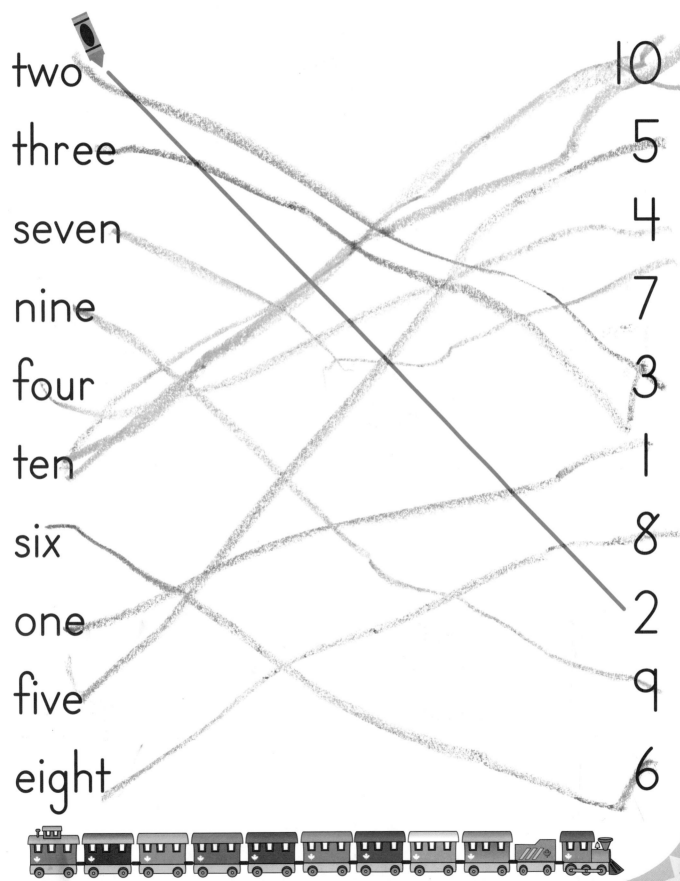

two	10
three	5
seven	4
nine	7
four	3
ten	1
six	8
one	2
five	9
eight	6

Fact families are groups of number sentences that show how numbers are related.
Example: 3 and 5 are related by these facts: 5 + 3 = 8

5 – 3 = 2

What numbers are in each fact family?
If you add these numbers to get 8 and subtract them to get 4, what are the numbers? _____ + _____ = 8

_____ – _____ = 4

If you add these numbers to get 7 and subtract them to get 5, what are the numbers? _____ + _____ = 7

_____ – _____ = 5

If you add these numbers to get 9 and subtract them to get 3, what are the numbers? _____ + _____ = 9

_____ – _____ = 3

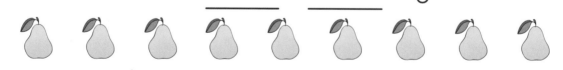

If you add these numbers to get 6 and subtract them to get 4, what are the numbers? _____ + _____ = 6

_____ – _____ = 4

A **double** is a number sentence in which you add a number to itself. Practise your double facts:

1 + 1 = 2	4 + 4 = 8	7 + 7 = 14
2 + 2 = 4	5 + 5 = 10	8 + 8 = 16
3 + 3 = 6	6 + 6 = 12	9 + 9 = 18

Know your double facts to help you solve other addition problems.

Use **doubles** to solve these addition problems.

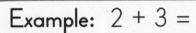

Example: 2 + 3 = Think: 2 + 2 = 4 2 + 3 is one more than 2 + 2 2 + 2 + 1 = 5 so 2 + 3 must be 5.	**Example:** 7 + 9 = Think: 7 + 7 = 14 7 + 9 is two more than 7 + 7 7 + 7 + 2 = 16 so 7 + 9 must be 16.

5 + 5 + 1 = ___

5 + 6 = ___

6 + 6 + 2 = ___

6 + 8 = ___

3 + 3 + 1 = ___

3 + 4 = ___

5 + 5 + 2 = ___

5 + 7 = ___

7 + 7 + 1 = ___

7 + 8 = ___

10 + 10 + 2 = ___

10 + 12 = ___

When adding numbers together, the answer is the sum. If the numbers in one column add up to more than 9, we need to regroup it. In addition, we regroup by making a ten out of ten ones.

Regrouping Examples:

• 10 can be shown as 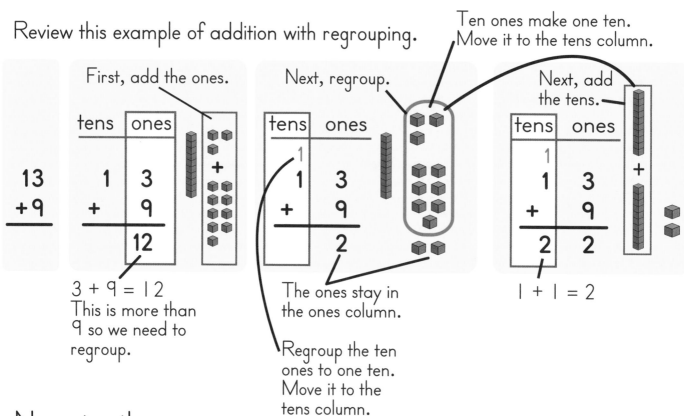 10 ones = 1 ten

• 13 can be shown as 13 ones = 1 ten and 3 ones

• 22 can be shown as 2 tens and 2 ones = 1 ten and 12 ones

Review this example of addition with regrouping.

First, add the ones.

tens	ones
1	3
+	9
	12

13
+9

3 + 9 = 12
This is more than 9 so we need to regroup.

Next, regroup.

tens	ones
1	
1	3
+	9
	2

The ones stay in the ones column.

Regroup the ten ones to one ten. Move it to the tens column.

Ten ones make one ten. Move it to the tens column.

Next, add the tens.

tens	ones
1	
1	3
+	9
2	2

1 + 1 = 2

Now, try these:

74	42	56	28	33	36	68
+17	+28	+35	+45	+58	+29	+22

Use regrouping to solve these word problems.

Example:

15 kids had hotdogs for lunch.

19 kids had pizza for lunch.

How many kids were having lunch?

```
  1
  15
+19
───
  34
```

Karen picked up 35 maple leaves.
Dave picked up 27 maple leaves.
How many maple leaves did Karen and Dave pick up?

Mike bought 42 jellybeans.
Cathy bought 58 jellybeans.
How many jellybeans did Mike and Cathy buy?

Ken shot 69 hockey pucks. Ron shot 23 hockey pucks.
How many hockey pucks did Ken and Ron shoot?

Georgia swam 27 metres. Vince swam 26 metres.
How many metres did they swim in all?

When subtracting numbers, the answer is the difference. If the top number in one column is smaller than the bottom number, we need to regroup. In subtraction, we regroup by breaking a ten into ten ones. See page 6 for examples.

Review this example of subtraction using regrouping.

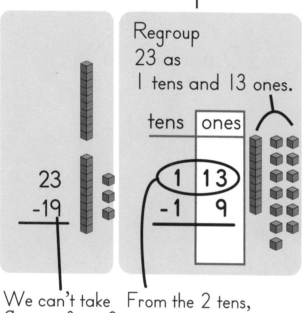

We can't take 9 away from 3 so we need to regroup the 23.

From the 2 tens, regroup one ten into ten ones. Move it to the ones column.
23 is now 1 ten and 13 ones.

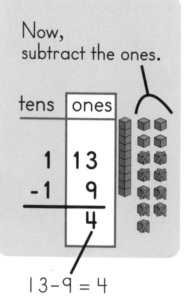

$13 - 9 = 4$

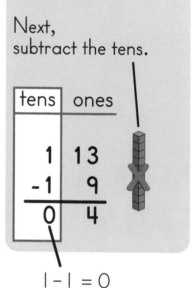

$1 - 1 = 0$

Now, try these:

38	26	23	20	63	42	33	75
- 19	-17	- 7	-14	-24	-25	-15	-25

Find the missing number for each problem using subtraction.

Connect the dots in the order they appear in your answers to questions 1 to 14.

Example:
45 + ____ = 79
Using subtraction:
79 – 45 = 34
Then:
45 + ㉞ = 79

1. 18 + ___ = 39

2. ___ + 33 = 65

3. 53 + ___ = 88

4. 30 + ___ = 42

5. ___ + 28 = 92

6. 38 + ___ = 54

7. ___ + 15 = 35

8. ___ + 56 = 67

9. 14 + ___ = 54

10. ___ + 31 = 72

11. 23 + ___ = 78

12. 13 + ___ = 32

13. ___ + 46 = 77

14. 24 + ___ = 66

Start ㉞ ● ● 42 End

21 ●

● 31

32 ●

35 ●

12 ●   ● 19

64 ●   ● 55

16 ●   20 ●   40 ●   ● 41

11 ●

9

Use subtraction to solve the word problems.

Example:

Mom baked 24 cookies. Dad ate 15 cookies. How many cookies are left?

$$\begin{array}{r} \overset{1\ 14}{\cancel{2}\cancel{4}} \\ -15 \\ \hline 9 \end{array}$$ Nine cookies are left.

Lily has 36 stickers. She used 17 of them. How many stickers does she have left?

A colouring book has 95 pages. Emily colours 49 pages. How many pages are left to colour?

Jeff has 12 golf balls. He loses 8 of them. How many golf balls does he have left?

The newspaper has 76 pages. Ben reads 47 pages. How many pages are left to read?

How many number pairs in the picture can you find that have a difference of 5? Circle the pairs on the Canadian grizzly bear. You should find 22 pairs. Two examples are circled to get you started.

A **fraction** is a part of a whole.

When an object is divided into 2 equal parts, it is divided in **half**.
We write a half as $\frac{1}{2}$.

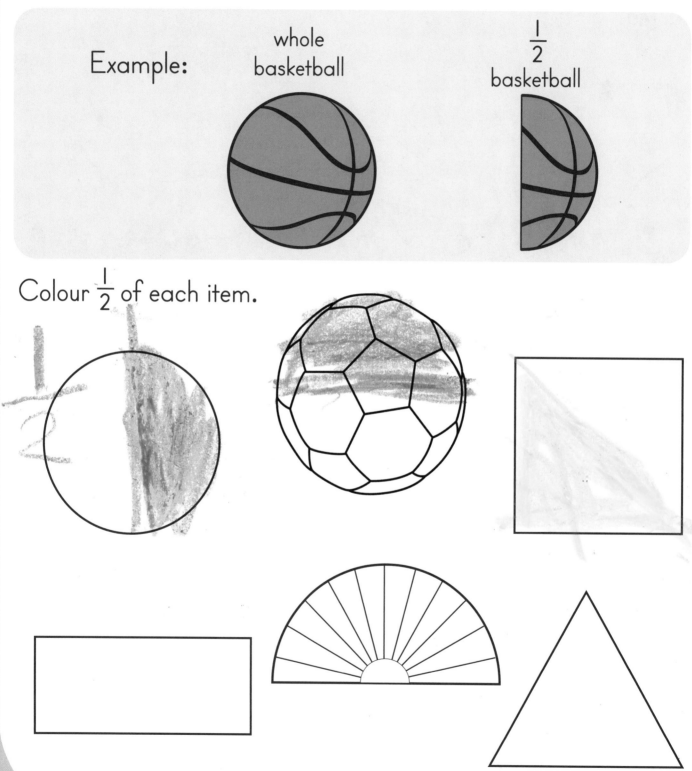

Example: whole basketball

$\frac{1}{2}$ basketball

Colour $\frac{1}{2}$ of each item.

When an object is divided into 3 equal parts, it is divided into thirds. We write a third as $\frac{1}{3}$.

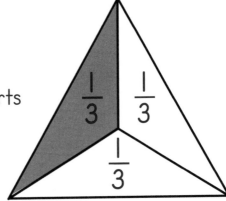

Example:
The triangle is divided into 3 equal parts (thirds).

Answer the questions.

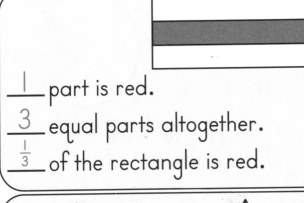

__1__ part is red.

__3__ equal parts altogether.

__$\frac{1}{3}$__ of the rectangle is red.

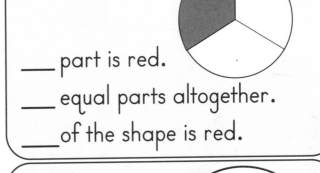

___ part is red.

___ equal parts altogether.

___ of the shape is red.

___ part is red.

___ equal parts altogether.

___ of the shape is red.

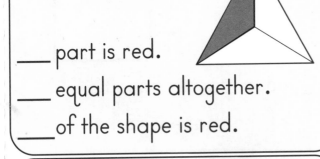

___ part is red.

___ equal parts altogether.

___ of the shape is red.

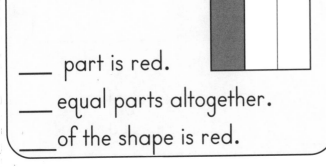

___ part is red.

___ equal parts altogether.

___ of the shape is red.

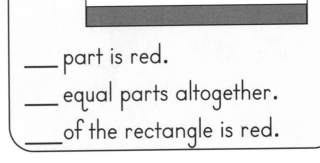

___ part is red.

___ equal parts altogether.

___ of the rectangle is red.

When an object is divided into 4 equal parts, it is divided into fourths. We write a fourth as $\frac{1}{4}$.

Example:

The square is divided into 4 equal parts (fourths).

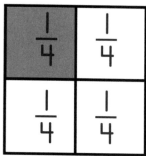

Answer the questions.

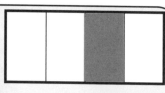

__1__ part is red.

__4__ equal parts altogether.

__$\frac{1}{4}$__ of the shape is red.

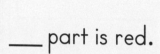

___ part is red.

___ equal parts altogether.

___ of the shape is red.

___ part is red.

___ equal parts altogether.

___ of the shape is red.

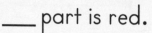

___ part is red.

___ equal parts altogether.

___ of the shape is red.

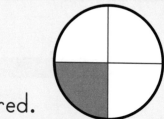

___ part is red.

___ equal parts altogether.

___ of the shape is red.

___ part is red.

___ equal parts altogether.

___ of the shape is red.

How much of each shape is **not coloured**? Write the fraction in each shape.

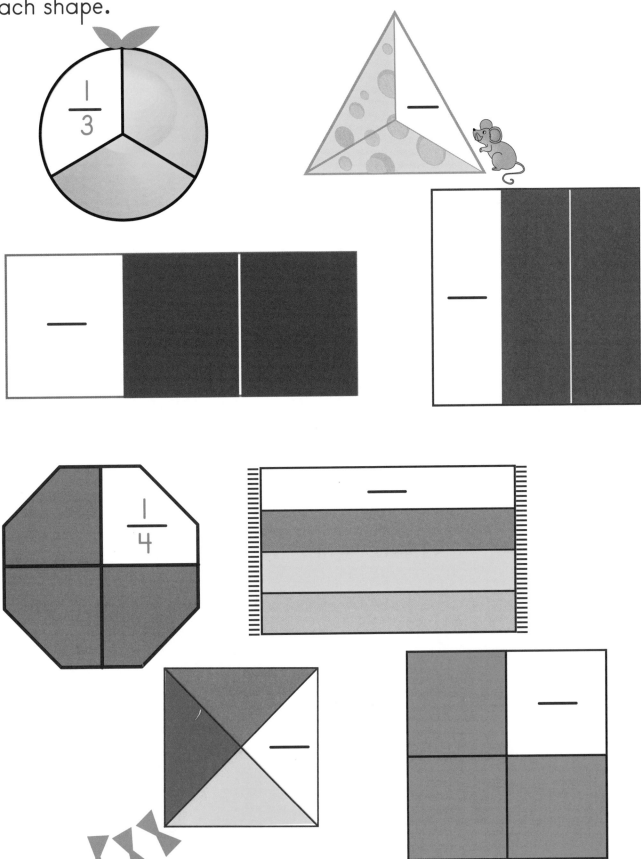

Multiplication is faster than addition!

$$6 + 6 + 6 = 18$$
$$3 \text{ sixes} = 18$$
$$3 \times 6 = 18$$

Add and multiply to solve these problems. Draw groups to help.

8 + 8 = _____

2 eights = _____

2 x 8 = _____

2 + 2 + 2 = _____

_____ twos = _____

_____ x 2 = _____

6 + 6 = _____

2 sixes = _____

2 x _____ = _____

6 + 6 + 6 + 6 + 6 = _____

_____ sixes = _____

_____ x 6 = _____

3 + 3 + 3 + 3 = _____

_____ threes = _____

_____ x 3 = _____

4 + 4 + 4 = _____

_____ fours = _____

_____ x 4 = _____

7 + 7 + 7 + 7 + 7 + 7 = _____

_____ sevens = _____

_____ x 7 = _____

8 + 8 + 8 = _____

_____ eights = _____

_____ x 8 = _____

5 + 5 + 5 + 5 = _____

_____ fives = _____

_____ x 5 = _____

9 + 9 + 9 + 9 + 9 = _____

_____ nines = _____

_____ x 9 = _____

Solve these problems using multiplication. Draw groups to help.

Example:

2 x 3

= 3 + 3 = 6

3  + 3

3 x 2

__ + __ + __ = ____

3 x 4

__ + __ + __ = ____

4 x 5

__ + __ + __ + __ = ____

3 x 5

__ + __ + __ = ____

2 x 7

__ + __ = ____

3 x 8

__ + __ + __ = ____

6 x 2

__ + __ + __ + __ + __ + __ = ____

3 x 9

__ + __ + __ = ____

5 x 2

__ + __ + __ + __ + __ = ____

3 x 7

__ + __ + __ = ____

2 x 5

__ + __ = ____

3 x 6

__ + __ + __ = ____

Multiply. Use the Key at the bottom to colour the picture.

6 x 1 = 6

2 x 3 =

9 x 3 =

3 x 9 =

4 x 2 = 8

3 x 2 =

3 x 7 =

2 x 8 =

3 x 3 =

9 x 2 =

Key

27 = green, 9 = yellow, 21 = pink, 6 = white, 16 = brown, 8 = orange, 18 = blue

penny = 1¢   dime = 10¢

nickel = 5¢   quarter = 25¢

Write the number of pennies for each coin. How many ¢?
I nickel = __5__ pennies = ___5__ ¢
I dime = ____ pennies = _____¢
I quarter = ____ pennies = _____¢

Write the number of nickels for each coin. How many ¢?
I dime = ____ nickels = _____¢
I quarter = ____ nickels = _____¢

Write the number of nickels and dimes in a quarter. How many ¢?
I quarter = ____ dimes + ____ nickels = _____¢

We can use different coins to pay for something.

Example:

Here are two ways to pay 35¢:

One way:

1 quarter
1 dime

Another way:

3 dimes
1 nickel

Show 2 ways to pay for each item.

60¢

One way:

_____ quarters

_____ dimes

_____ nickels

_____ pennies

Another way:

_____ quarters

_____ dimes

_____ nickels

_____ pennies

45¢

One way:

_____ quarters

_____ dimes

_____ nickels

_____ pennies

Another way:

_____ quarters

_____ dimes

_____ nickels

_____ pennies

Money Game

How to Play:

1. Find a friend, two game pieces, paper & a pencil, and a coin to flip.
2. Flip the coin. Whoever gets heads goes first. Then take turns.
3. When it lands on heads, move forward one space.
4. When it lands on tails, move forward two spaces.
5. When you land on a space with a coin, write down that amount for your score. Follow the instruction on other spaces.
6. Continue to add to or subtract from your score as you play.
7. The first one to get to $2 wins.

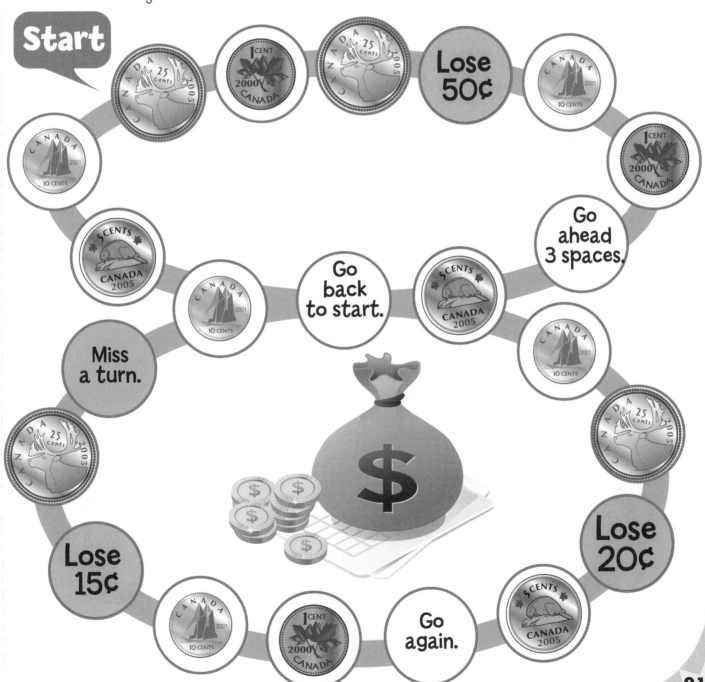

A clock has a big hand and a little hand. The the little hand tells the hour. The big hand tells the minutes.

On this clock, the little hand points to 3. The hour is 3.
The big hand points to 12. This is no minutes past the hour. We write this as :00.
It is 3 o'clock or 3:00.

What time is it? 3 o'clock or 3:00

A digital clock shows the time with numbers instead of hands. The green number on the left tells the hour.
The red number on the right tells the minutes after the hour. It is 3:00 or 3 o'clock.

What time is it? 3 o'clock or 3:00

Show the time. Use green for the hour. Use red for the minutes.

9 o'clock.

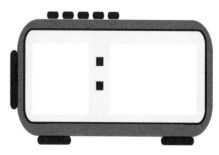

9 o'clock.

Colour the **little hour hands green** and the **big minute hands red**.
Tell the time 2 ways.

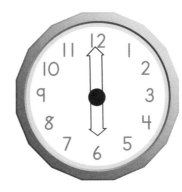

___ o'clock

__ : __

___ o'clock

__ : __

___ o'clock

__ : __

Colour the **hour numbers green** and the **minute numbers red**.

___ o'clock

___ o'clock

___ o'clock

Show the time. Use **green** for the hour. Use **red** for the minutes.

1 o'clock.

12 o'clock.

10 o'clock.

A full hour is 60 minutes. A half hour is 30 minutes. There are 2 halves in one hour. Look at the example. The little hour hand points just past the 3. The hour is 3. The big minute hand is half way around the clock at 6. It is **half past three** or **3:30**.

half past ___3___

___3___ : ___30___

half past _____

_____ : _____

half past _____

_____ : _____

half past _____

_____ : _____

half past _____

_____ : _____

half past _____

_____ : _____

A quarter hour is 15 minutes. There are 4 quarters in one hour.

Start at 12. Skip count by 5's around the clock to count the minutes. When you count 15, you will be at 3. When you count 30, you will be at 6. When you count 45, you will be at 9. When you count 60 you will be back at 12.

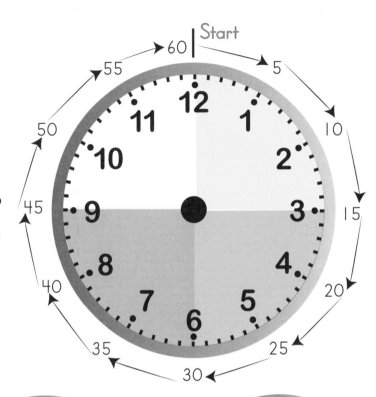

The little hand points just past 7. The hour is still 7. The big minute hand points to 3. To count the minutes past the hour, start at 12. Skip count by 5's to count 15 minutes. It is 7:15.

The little hand points past 7 but not yet to 8. The hour is still 7. The big minute hand has moved from 3 to 6. Another 15 minutes or quarter hour has passed. To count the minutes, skip count from 12 again. It is 7:30.

The little hand points past 7 but not yet to 8. The hour is still 7. The big minute hand has moved from 6 to 9. Another 15 minutes or quarter hour has passed. To count the minutes, skip count from 12 again. It is 7:45 or a quarter to 8.

When the minute hand is a quarter of the way around the clock pointing to 3 we say it is **quarter past the hour** or **something : 15.** Write the time 2 ways.

quarter past __1__   quarter past _____   quarter past _____

__1__ : __15__   ____ : ____   ____ : ____

When the minute hand points to 9, we say it is **quarter to the hour** or **something :45.** Write the time 2 ways.

quarter to __3__   quarter to _____   quarter to _____

__2__ : __45__   ____ : ____   ____ : ____

1:15	11:45
quarter past _____	quarter to _____
____ : ____	____ : ____

In what order did these events happen?
Write the letters in sequence order on the lines below the pictures.

The correct order is:

First _____   Second _____   Third _____   Fourth _____

27

Follow the clues to find out which day in September will be the first day of school. Cross out any date that is not the first day of school.

The first day of school is not on a Thursday, Friday, Saturday, or Sunday.

The first day of school is not on any day that begins with a 2.

The date does not end in a 0 or 8.

The date is before September 14, but after September 8.

What date is the first day of school? _____

September						
Sunday	Monday	Tuesday	Wednesday	Thursday	Friday	Saturday
	1	2	3	4	5	6
7	8	9	10	11	12	13
14	15	16	17	18	19	20
21	22	23	24	25	26	27
28	29	30				

Cut out the ruler.

Use it to measure each object below.

_____ cm

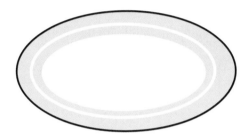

_____ cm

_____ cm

These objects can be found around your house. Find each object and measure it to the nearest cm (centimetre).

pencil _____ cm

book _____ cm

fork _____ cm

telephone _____ cm

shoe _____ cm

Write the length of each line in centimetres.

_____ cm

_____ cm

_____ cm

_____ cm

_____ cm

Centimetres are larger than millimetres.
There are 10 millimetres in one centimetre.

10 mm = |||||||||| 1 cm = ||||||||||

0   10 mm   0   1 cm

Look at the measurement of each line. Circle **mm** or **cm** to show the correct unit used.

This line is 45   cm   mm

This line is 8   cm   mm

This line is 96   cm   mm

Measure each item. Use the ruler from page 29 or find one at home. Circle the units you use.

_____ cm   mm   _____ cm   mm

_____ cm   mm   _____ cm   mm

Perimeter is the measurement of the distance **around the outside** of a shape. The perimeter of a shape is found by counting how many cells are around the shape.

Count the cells around each shape.

Example:

14 cells

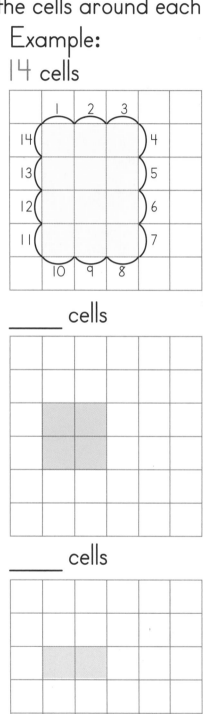

____ cells

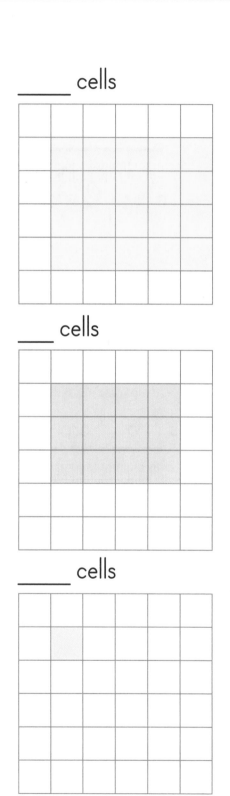

____ cells

____ cells

____ cells

____ cells

Area is the measurement of the amount of surface a shape covers.
Area is found by counting **how many cells are inside** each shape.

Count the cells inside each shape. One has been started for you.
Example:

__13__ cells

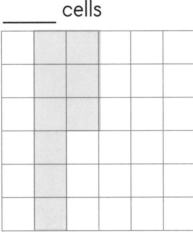

_____ cells

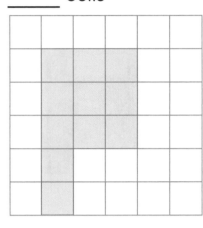

_____ cells

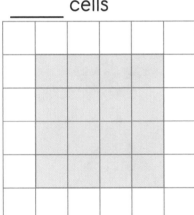

_____ cells

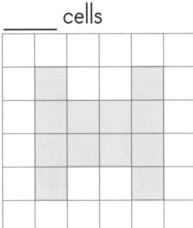

_____ cells

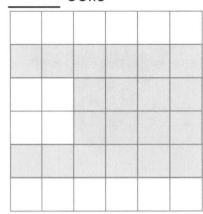

_____ cells

Draw your own shape. Determine the area by counting the cells.
Colour them.

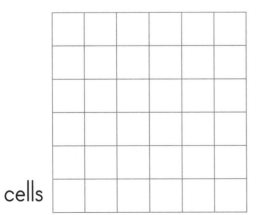

_____ cells

_____ cells

Draw a line from each shape word to the matching shape.

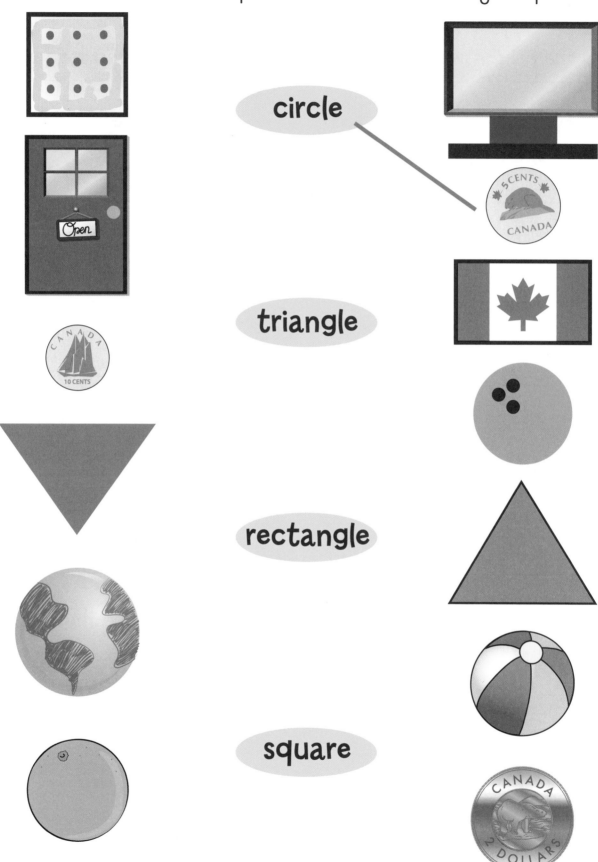

circle

triangle

rectangle

square

Use an orange crayon to colour all the triangles.

Use a yellow crayon to colour all the circles.

Use a green crayon to colour all the ovals.

Use a blue crayon to colour all the squares.

Use a red crayon to colour all the rectangles.

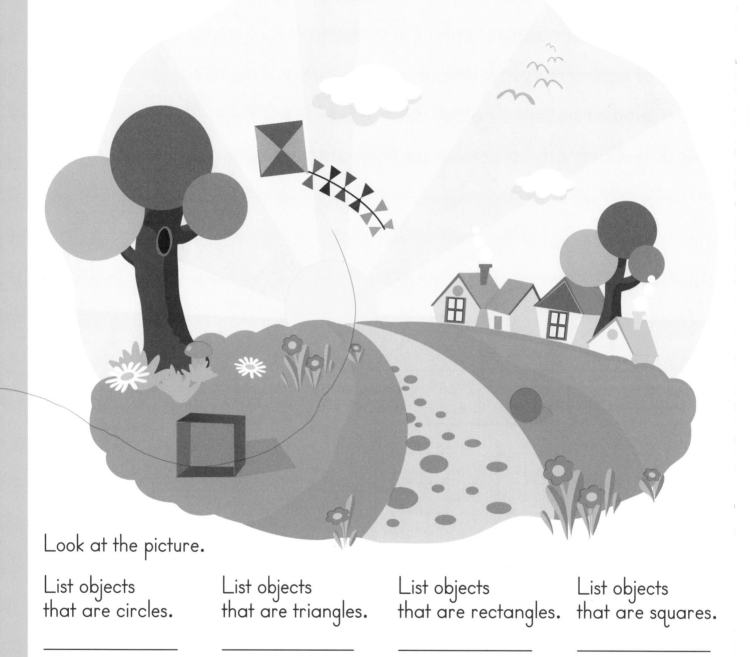

Look at the picture.

List objects that are circles.	List objects that are triangles.	List objects that are rectangles.	List objects that are squares.
_____	_____	_____	_____
_____	_____	_____	_____
_____	_____	_____	_____
_____	_____	_____	_____
_____	_____	_____	_____
_____	_____	_____	_____

A **quadrilateral** is a figure with four sides.

A **trapezoid** is a quadrilateral with one set of parallel sides.

A **parallelogram** is a quadrilateral with two sets of parallel sides.

Parallel sides are two sides that are opposite each other and go in the same direction. Example:

The red lines are parallel sides.
The blue lines are parallel sides.

Circle the name of each shape. Use the letter next to the name to solve the riddle.

1.

P trapezoid
I square
L triangle

2.

F rectangle
S parallelogram
T trapezoid

3.

A square
S rectangle
U triangle

4.

Y parallelogram
Z square
J circle

5.

K circle
G square
O parallelogram

6.

U parallelogram
H triangle
O trapezoid

Riddle:
If your mother has a baby, but it's not your brother and it's not your sister, who is it?

$\dfrac{\quad}{1}$ $\dfrac{\quad}{2}$ $\dfrac{\quad}{3}$, $\dfrac{\quad}{4}$ $\dfrac{\quad}{5}$ $\dfrac{\quad}{6}$!

Geometry and Spatial Sense – Name the Shapes

A **triangle** is a figure with three sides.

A **quadrilateral** is a figure with four sides.

A **pentagon** is a figure with five sides.

A **hexagon** is a figure with six sides.

A **heptagon** is a figure with seven sides.

An **octagon** is a figure with eight sides.

Write the number of sides for each shape name on the line. Then colour the correct shape to match the colour of the name.

Shape Name	Number of Sides	Shape
quadrilateral	_____	
triangle	**3**	
octagon	_____	
pentagon	_____	
heptagon	_____	
hexagon	_____	

Let's draw a cube.

 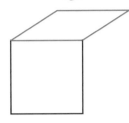 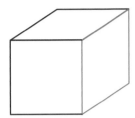 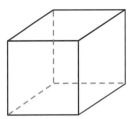

| Trace the square. | Add a quadrilateral along top of square. | Add another quadrilateral along the side of square. | With dotted lines add a quadrilateral for the base and another quadrilateral to make 6 sides altogether. |

Let's draw a pyramid.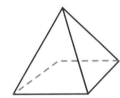

  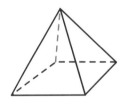 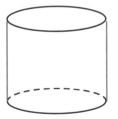

Trace the triangle.

Add a triangle along the side.

Add dotted lines to make a square base.

With dotted lines add a line from the corner to the top to make a square base pyramid.

Let's draw a cylinder.

Trace the oval.

Add a second oval below it.

Add 2 straight lines to join the ovals.

Now practice all 3 shapes on another piece of paper.

A **flip** is a transformation where an image is turned over a line. The flipped image has the same angle, length, and size as the original image, but it is flipped in another direction. Example:

Draw the flip to show the other position.

Draw the flip to show the other position.

A slide is a transformation that moves an image in a straight line to make a copy of the image in another location.

Example:

Draw a slide of each image to the right of the original.

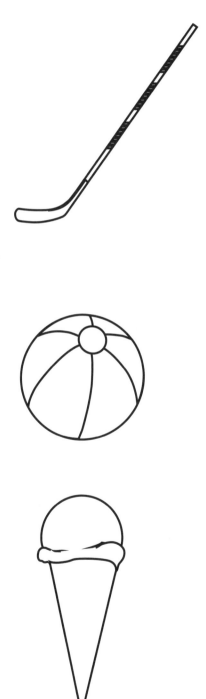

Symmetry is shown when one side of an object is the mirror image of the other side.

Examples:

In these pictures, half of an object is missing. Draw the missing half so the shape is symmetrical. Colour the picture.

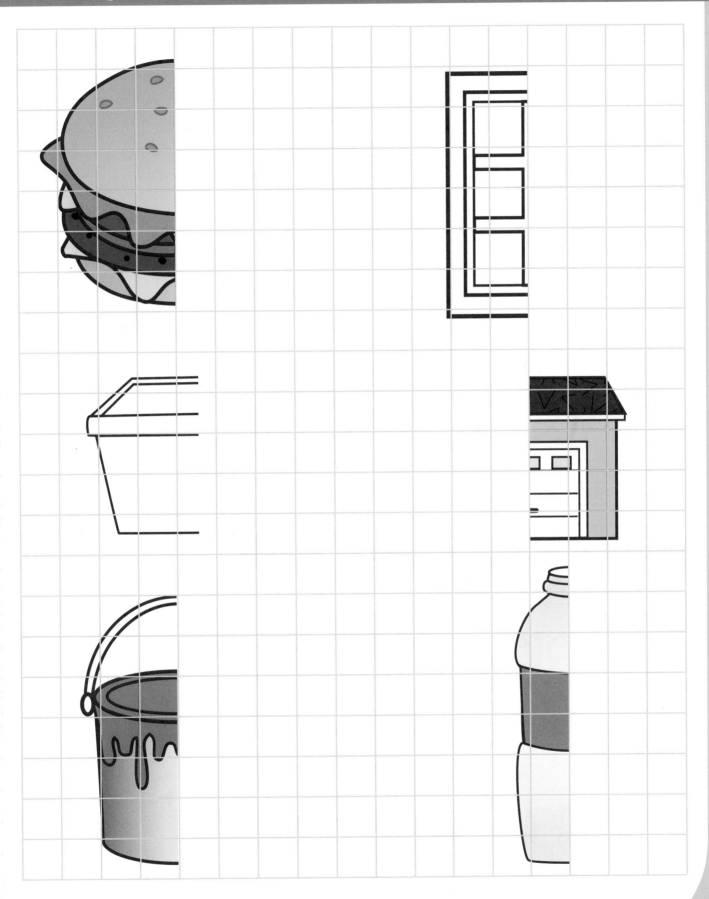

Look at each pattern and description. Put a ✓ in the box if the description matches the pattern. Put an X in the box if it doesn't.

An apple is followed by one A and 2 Bs.

🍎ABB 🍎ABB 🍎ABB 🍎

A cone is followed by 3 As and 2 Bs

▲ AAABB ▲ AAABB ▲ AAABB ▲

Every third object is a C.

ABCABCABC

Every third object is one maple leaf.

Three pairs of scissors are followed by two paper clips.

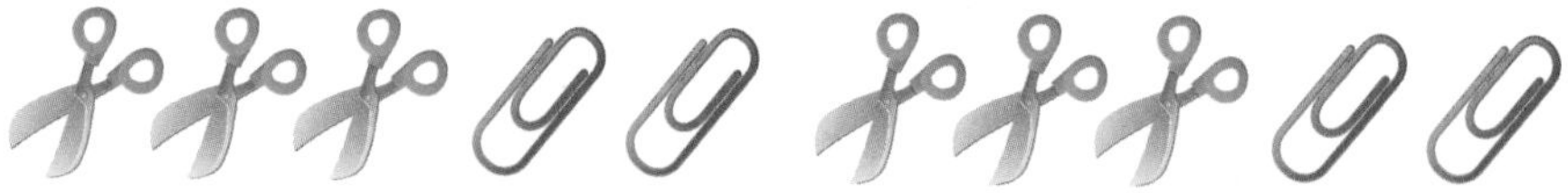

Every second object is an apple.

Circle the pattern that **adds 5** each time.

$$\boxed{4, 9, 14, 19} \qquad 15, 14, 13, 12 \qquad 15, 17, 20, 23$$

4+5 = 9   9+5=14   14+5=19

Circle the pattern that **subtracts 4** each time.

$$5, 7, 9, 11 \qquad 21, 17, 13, 9 \qquad 24, 19, 14, 9$$

Circle the pattern that **adds 7** each time.

$$12, 14, 16, 18 \qquad 8, 14, 20, 26 \qquad 23, 30, 37, 44$$

Create your own pattern.

Create a growing pattern that **adds 3** each time.

_____

Create a shrinking pattern that **subtracts 10** each time.

_____

Pattern Game

How to Play:

1. Find a friend, two game pieces, and a coin to flip.
2. Flip the coin.
3. When it lands on heads, move forward four spaces.
4. When it lands on tails, move forward one space.
5. Follow the instructions on the shape you land on.
6. The first one to reach the finish wins.
7. Bee cells are out of bounds. Stay on the blue path.

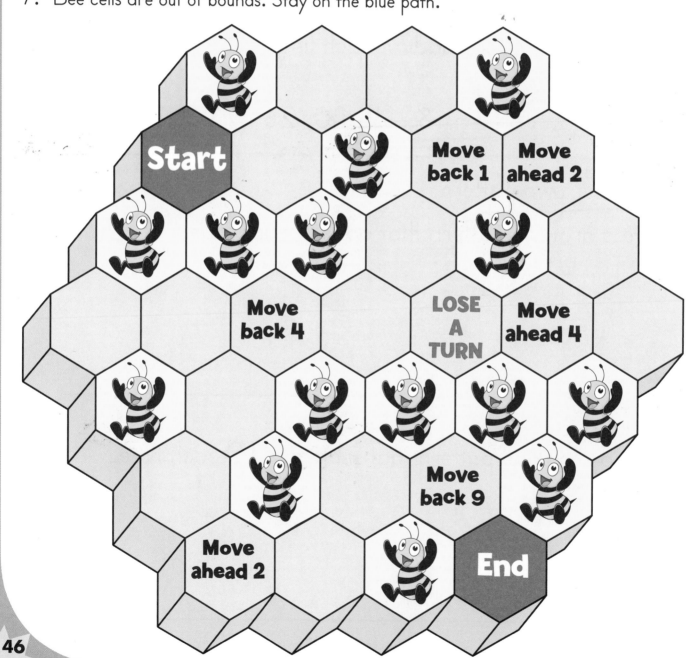

Skip count the bees from flower to flower.

Skip count by 5's the rain drops from cloud to cloud.

Ten people live in each building. Skip count by 10's to find out how many people live on the street all together.

30

Patterning and Algebra – Skip Counting by 10's

Skip count from the start number in the blue box. Move down, right, left, or diagonally until you land on an object. Answers may vary.

What object do you land on when you start at 2 and skip count by 2?

_____

What object do you land on when you start at 5 and skip count by 5?

_____

What object do you land on when you start at 3 and skip count by 3?

_____

What object do you land on when you start at 4 and skip count by 4?

_____

2	4	7	5	3	6
7	8	6	8	10	9
9	12	10	12	15	12
16	12	14	20	21	18
14	20	25	16	18	24
16	30	24	28	20	27
35	18	32	17	22	30
40	20	24	36	33	24

Probability is the likelihood that something will happen.

Examples:
When we flip a coin,
we end up with 1 of 2 outcomes:
Heads or Tails.

Heads   Tails

This spinner works the same way. When we spin the arrow, it lands on either Heads or Tails. There are 2 possible outcomes. The arrow can land on only 1. We say the probability that the arrow will land on heads:

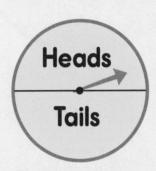

$$\frac{1}{2}$$

1 — Number of sections with Heads
— out of
2 — Total number of sections

Look at the spinner. Answer the questions.

How many sections are blue? _____

How many sections are red? _____

How many sections all together? _____

What is the likelihood of landing on red?

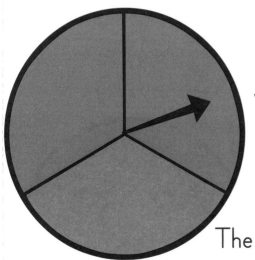

$$\frac{2}{3}$$

2 — Number of sections with red
— out of
3 — Total number of sections

The likelihood of the arrow landing on red is 2/3.

What is the likelihood of landing on blue?

— Number of sections with blue
— — out of
— Total number of sections

Look at the spinner. Answer the questions.

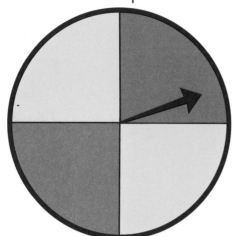

How many sections are yellow? _____

How many sections are blue? _____

How many sections are red? _____

How many sections all together? _____

What is the likelihood that the arrow will land on yellow?

— Number of sections with yellow
   out of
   Total number of sections

On blue?

— Number of sections with blue
   out of
   Total number of sections

On red?

— Number of sections with red
   out of
   Total number of sections

It is **more likely** that the arrow will land on the largest section.

It is **less likely** that the arrow will land on the smallest section.

It is **equally likely** that the arrow will land on sections that are the same size.

On what objects is the arrow **equally likely** to land? _____

On what object is the arrow **least likely** to land? _____

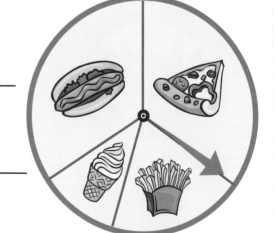

Riddle:
Where does a penguin keep his money?

Determine the probability for each question below.
Circle the letter under each answer. Use that letter to solve the riddle.

Question #1
Winning a game of x's and o's when playing with a friend.

$\frac{1}{2}$ $\frac{1}{3}$ $\frac{1}{6}$

A   **S**   **7**

Question #2
Getting a 3 when rolling a die cube.

$\frac{1}{2}$ $\frac{2}{3}$ $\frac{1}{6}$

C   **B**   **N**

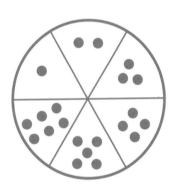

Question #3
If you have 3 red marbles and 1 blue marble in a jar,
what are the chances of drawing a blue marble from the jar?

$\frac{3}{5}$ $\frac{1}{4}$ $\frac{2}{4}$

P   **S**   **O**

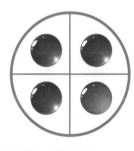

Use the letters that go with each answer to solve the riddle.
Write the letter from each answer above on the matching line below.

Riddle Solution:

____ ____ ____ __O_ _W_ __B_ __ __ _K_
Q1   Q3   Q2   Q1 Q2

Count the dog bones below in each column. Colour the boxes
to show how many dog bones the dog has eaten
on 5 different days.

Tally marks are used to record data. Count the tally marks to answer the questions.

Players Names	Total Goals Scored
Tim	‖‖‖ ‖
Jane	‖‖
Josh	‖‖‖ ‖‖‖ ‖‖‖ ‖
Mary	‖‖‖ ‖‖
Brent	‖‖‖ ‖‖‖ ‖‖
Dan	‖

Which player scored the most goals? Josh

Which player scored only two goals? Dan

How many more goals did Brent score over Mary? 5

Which two players scored as many goals together as Josh did by himself?
Brent and Jane

Solutions

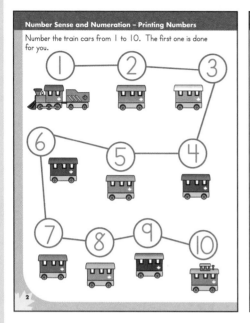

Page 2

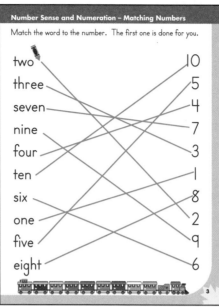

Page 3

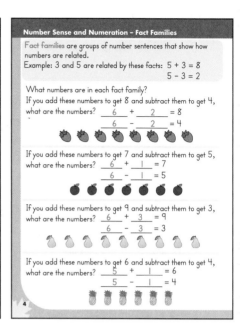

Page 4

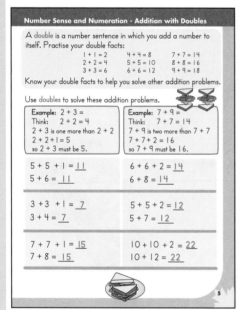

Page 5

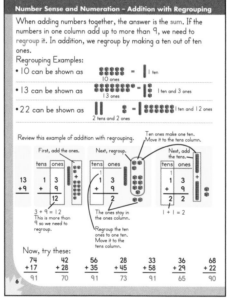

Page 6

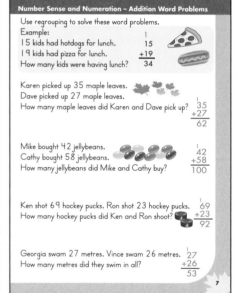

Page 7

Solutions

Page 8

When subtracting numbers, the answer is the difference. If the top number in one column is smaller than the bottom number, we need to regroup. In subtraction, we regroup by breaking a ten into ten ones. See page 6 for examples.

Review this example of subtraction using regrouping.

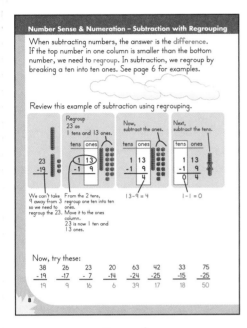

Regroup 23 as 1 tens and 13 ones.

tens	ones
1	13
-1	9

23
-19

We can't take 9 away from 3 so we need to regroup the 23.

From the 2 tens, regroup one ten into ten ones. Move it to the ones column. 23 is now 1 ten and 13 ones.

Now, subtract the ones.
13-9 = 4

Next, subtract the tens.
1-1 = 0

Now, try these:

38	26	23	20	63	42	33	75
-19	-17	- 7	-14	-24	-25	-15	-25
19	9	16	6	39	17	18	50

Page 8

Page 9

Find the missing number for each problem using subtraction.

Connect the dots in the order they appear in your answers to questions 1 to 14.

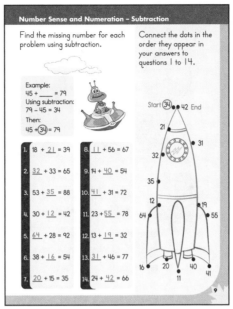

Example:
45 + ___ = 79
Using subtraction:
79 – 45 = 34
Then:
45 + (34) = 79

1. 18 + 21 = 39
2. 32 + 33 = 65
3. 53 + 35 = 88
4. 30 + 12 = 42
5. 64 + 28 = 92
6. 38 + 16 = 54
7. 20 + 15 = 35
8. 11 + 56 = 67
9. 14 + 40 = 54
10. 41 + 31 = 72
11. 23 + 55 = 78
12. 13 + 19 = 32
13. 31 + 46 = 77
14. 24 + 42 = 66

Page 9

Page 10

Use subtraction to solve the word problems.

Example:
Mom baked 24 cookies. Dad ate 15 cookies. How many cookies are left?

1 14
2̶4̶
– 1 5
9   Nine cookies are left.

Lily has 36 stickers. She used 17 of them. How many stickers does she have left?

2 16
3̶6̶
– 1 7
1 9   She has 19 stickers left.

A colouring book has 95 pages. Emily colours 49 pages. How many pages are left to colour?

8 15
9̶5̶
– 4 9
4 6   46 pages are left to colour.

Jeff has 12 golf balls. He loses 8 of them. How many golf balls does he have left?

0 12
1̶2̶
–   8
4   He has 4 golf balls left.

The newspaper has 76 pages. Ben reads 47 pages. How many pages are left to read?

6 16
7̶6̶
– 4 7
2 9   29 pages are left to read.

Page 10

Page 11

How many number pairs in the picture can you find that have a difference of 5? Circle the pairs on the Canadian grizzly bear. You should find 22 pairs. Two examples are circled to get you started.

Page 11

Page 12

A fraction is a part of a whole.
When an object is divided into 2 equal parts, it is divided in half. We write a half as $\frac{1}{2}$.

Example:

whole basketball

$\frac{1}{2}$ basketball

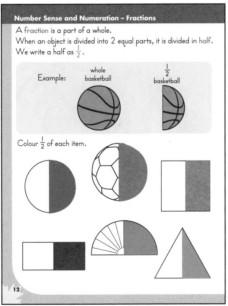

Colour $\frac{1}{2}$ of each item.

Page 12

Page 13

When an object is divided into 3 equal parts, it is divided into thirds. We write a third as $\frac{1}{3}$.

Example:
The triangle is divided into 3 equal parts (thirds).

$\frac{1}{3}$ $\frac{1}{3}$ $\frac{1}{3}$

Answer the questions.

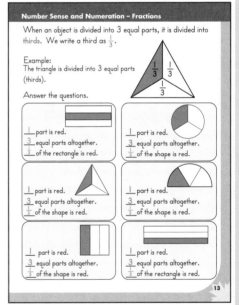

1 part is red.
3 equal parts altogether.
$\frac{1}{3}$ of the rectangle is red.

1 part is red.
3 equal parts altogether.
$\frac{1}{3}$ of the shape is red.

1 part is red.
3 equal parts altogether.
$\frac{1}{3}$ of the shape is red.

1 part is red.
3 equal parts altogether.
$\frac{1}{3}$ of the shape is red.

1 part is red.
3 equal parts altogether.
$\frac{1}{3}$ of the shape is red.

1 part is red.
3 equal parts altogether.
$\frac{1}{3}$ of the rectangle is red.

Page 13

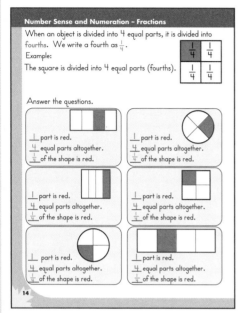

Page 14

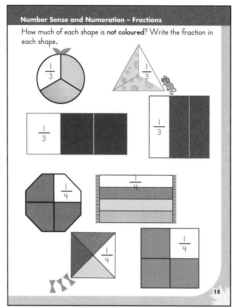

Page 15

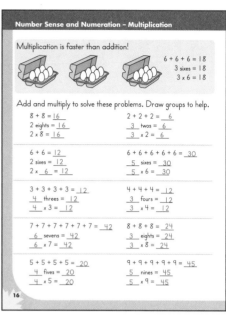

Page 16

Page 17

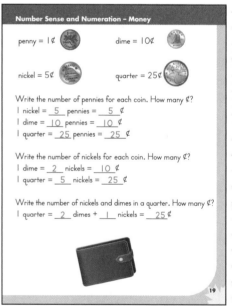

Page 18

Page 19

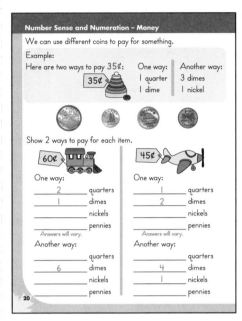

Page 20

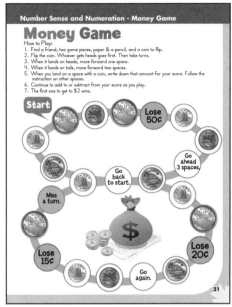

Page 21

Page 22

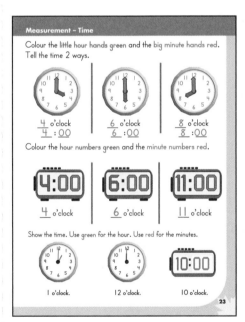

Page 23

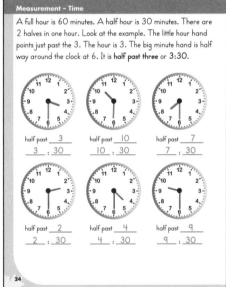

Page 24

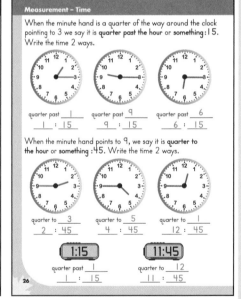

Page 26

Solutions

Measurement Time – Sequencing

In what order did these events happen?
Write the letters in sequence order on the lines below the pictures.

The correct order is:
First **D**   Second **B**   Third **C**   Fourth **A**

Page 27

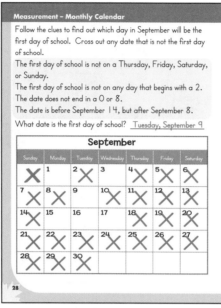

Measurement – Monthly Calendar

Follow the clues to find out which day in September will be the first day of school. Cross out any date that is not the first day of school.

The first day of school is not on a Thursday, Friday, Saturday, or Sunday.
The first day of school is not on any day that begins with a 2.
The date does not end in a 0 or 8.
The date is before September 14, but after September 8.

What date is the first day of school? _Tuesday, September 9_

Page 28

Measurement – Centimetres and Millimetres

Cut out the ruler.
Use it to measure each object below.

_2_ cm

_6_ cm

_6_ cm

These objects can be found around your house.
Find each object and measure it to the nearest cm (centimetre).

pencil _____ cm
book _____ cm
fork _____ cm
telephone _____ cm
shoe _____ cm

Answer will vary.

Page 29

Measurement – Centimetres and Millimetres

Write the length of each line in centimetres.

_4_ cm

_7_ cm

_10_ cm

_8_ cm

_2_ cm

Page 30

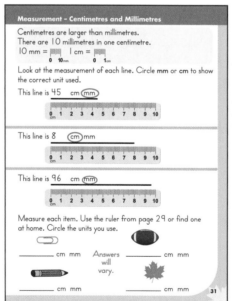

Measurement – Centimetres and Millimetres

Centimetres are larger than millimetres.
There are 10 millimetres in one centimetre.
10 mm = | 1 cm =

Look at the measurement of each line. Circle **mm** or **cm** to show the correct unit used.

This line is 45 cm (mm)

This line is 8 (cm) mm

This line is 96 cm (mm)

Measure each item. Use the ruler from page 29 or find one at home. Circle the units you use.

_____ cm mm   _____ cm mm
_____ cm mm   _____ cm mm

Answers will vary.

Page 31

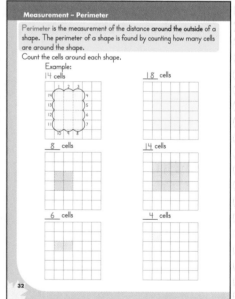

Measurement – Perimeter

Perimeter is the measurement of the distance **around the outside** of a shape. The perimeter of a shape is found by counting how many cells are around the shape.
Count the cells around each shape.

Example:
_14_ cells   _18_ cells

_8_ cells   _14_ cells

_6_ cells   _4_ cells

Page 32

Solutions

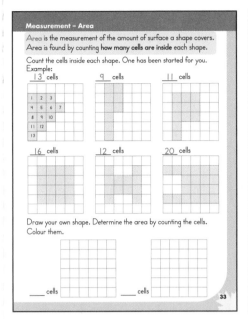

Page 33

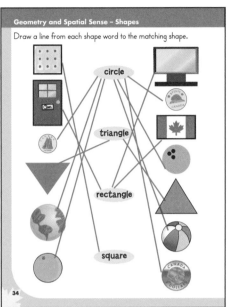

Page 34

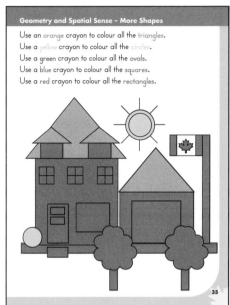

Page 35

Page 36

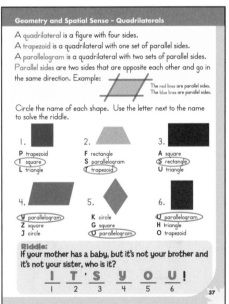

Page 37

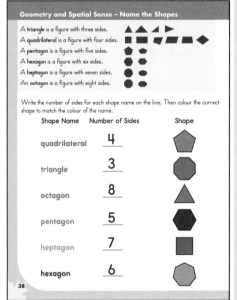

Page 38

Solutions

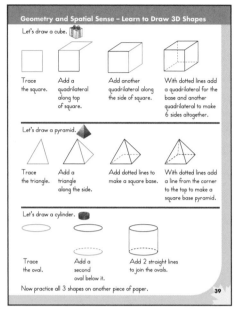

Page 39

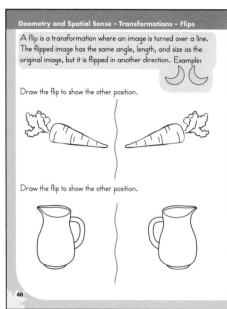

Page 40

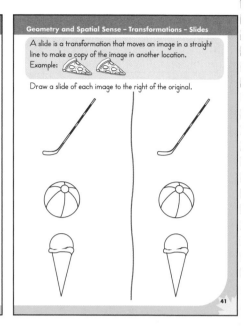

Page 41

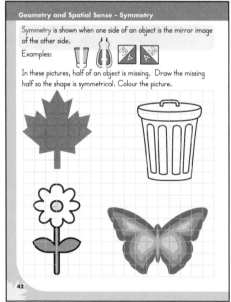

Page 42

Page 43

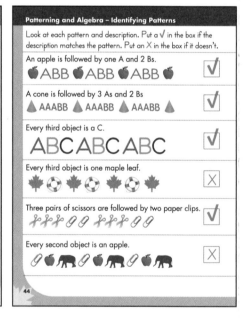

Page 44

Solutions

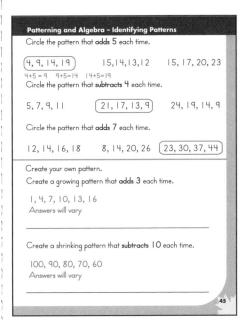

Patterning and Algebra – Identifying Patterns

Circle the pattern that **adds 5** each time.

4, 9, 14, 19   15, 14, 13, 12   15, 17, 20, 23

4+5 = 9   9+5=14   14+5=19

Circle the pattern that **subtracts 4** each time.

5, 7, 9, 11   **21, 17, 13, 9**   24, 19, 14, 9

Circle the pattern that **adds 7** each time.

12, 14, 16, 18   8, 14, 20, 26   **23, 30, 37, 44**

Create your own pattern.

Create a growing pattern that **adds 3** each time.

1, 4, 7, 10, 13, 16
Answers will vary

Create a shrinking pattern that **subtracts 10** each time.

100, 90, 80, 70, 60
Answers will vary

Page 45

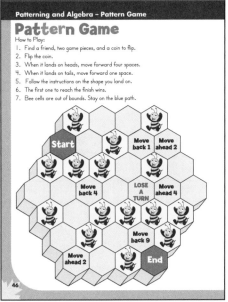

Patterning and Algebra – Pattern Game

Pattern Game

How to Play:
1. Find a friend, two game pieces, and a coin to flip.
2. Flip the coin.
3. When it lands on heads, move forward four spaces.
4. When it lands on tails, move forward one space.
5. Follow the instructions on the shape you land on.
6. The first one to reach the finish wins.
7. Bee cells are out of bounds. Stay on the blue path.

Page 46

Patterning and Algebra – Skip Counting by 2's

Skip count the bees from flower to flower.

Page 47

Patterning and Algebra – Skip Counting by 5's

Skip count by 5's the rain drops from cloud to cloud.

Page 48

Patterning and Algebra – Skip Counting by 10's

Ten people live in each building. Skip count by 10's to find out how many people live on the street all together.

Page 49

Patterning and Algebra – Skip Counting Game

Skip count from the start number in the blue box. Move down, right, left, or diagonally until you land on an object. Answers may vary.

What object do you land on when you start at 2 and skip count by 2?
drink and apple

What object do you land on when you start at 5 and skip count by 5?
basketball

What object do you land on when you start at 3 and skip count by 3?
calculator

What object do you land on when you start at 4 and skip count by 4?
banana

2	4	7	5	3	6
7	8	6	8	10	9
9	12	10	12	15	12
16	12	14	20	21	18
14	20	25	16	18	24
16	30	24	28	20	27
35	18	32	17	22	30
40	20	24	36	33	24

Page 50

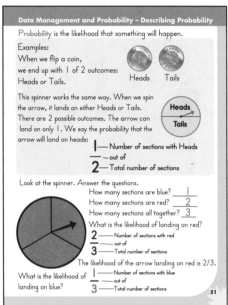

Data Management and Probability – Describing Probability

Probability is the likelihood that something will happen.

Examples:
When we flip a coin, we end up with 1 of 2 outcomes: Heads or Tails.

Heads   Tails

This spinner works the same way. When we spin the arrow, it lands on either Heads or Tails. There are 2 possible outcomes. The arrow can land on only 1. We say the probability that the arrow will land on heads:

$\dfrac{1}{2}$ — Number of sections with Heads — out of — Total number of sections

Look at the spinner. Answer the questions.
How many sections are blue? __1__
How many sections are red? __2__
How many sections all together? __3__
What is the likelihood of landing on red?

$\dfrac{2}{3}$ — Number of sections with red — out of — Total number of sections

The likelihood of the arrow landing on red is 2/3.

What is the likelihood of landing on blue? $\dfrac{1}{3}$ — Number of sections with blue — out of — Total number of sections

51

Page 51

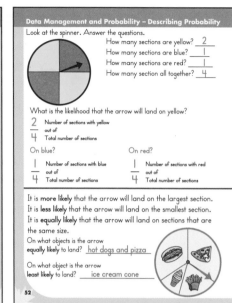

Data Management and Probability – Describing Probability

Look at the spinner. Answer the questions.
How many sections are yellow? __2__
How many sections are blue? __1__
How many sections are red? __1__
How many section all together? __4__

What is the likelihood that the arrow will land on yellow?

$\dfrac{2}{4}$ — Number of sections with yellow — out of — Total number of sections

On blue? $\dfrac{1}{4}$ — Number of sections with blue — out of — Total number of sections

On red? $\dfrac{1}{4}$ — Number of sections with red — out of — Total number of sections

It is **more likely** that the arrow will land on the largest section. It is **less likely** that the arrow will land on the smallest section. It is **equally likely** that the arrow will land on sections that are the same size.

On what objects is the arrow **equally likely** to land? __hot dogs and pizza__

On what object is the arrow **least likely** to land? __ice cream cone__

52

Page 52

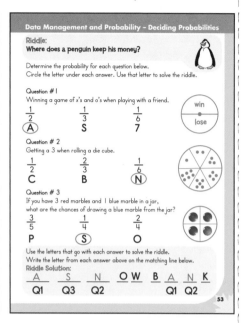

Data Management and Probability – Deciding Probabilities

Riddle:
Where does a penguin keep his money?

Determine the probability for each question below. Circle the letter under each answer. Use that letter to solve the riddle.

Question #1
Winning a game of x's and o's when playing with a friend.
$\dfrac{1}{2}$ (A) $\dfrac{1}{3}$ S $\dfrac{1}{6}$ 7

win / lose

Question #2
Getting a 3 when rolling a die cube.
$\dfrac{1}{2}$ C $\dfrac{2}{3}$ B $\dfrac{1}{6}$ (N)

Question #3
If you have 3 red marbles and 1 blue marble in a jar, what are the chances of drawing a blue marble from the jar?
$\dfrac{3}{5}$ P $\dfrac{1}{4}$ (S) $\dfrac{2}{4}$ O

Use the letters that go with each answer to solve the riddle. Write the letter from each answer above on the matching line below.
Riddle Solution:
<u>A</u> <u>S</u> <u>N</u> <u>O</u>W <u>B</u> <u>A</u> <u>N</u> <u>K</u>
Q1 Q3 Q2   Q1 Q2

53

Page 53

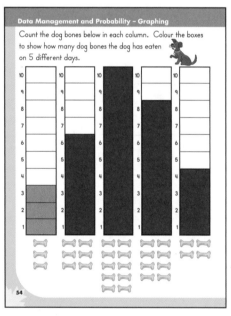

Data Management and Probability – Graphing

Count the dog bones below in each column. Colour the boxes to show how many dog bones the dog has eaten on 5 different days.

54

Page 54

Data Management and Probability – Tally Marks

Tally marks are used to record data. Count the tally marks to answer the questions.

Players Names	Total Goals Scored
Tim	ЦНТ ||
Jane	|||
Josh	ЦНТ ЦНТ ЦНТ	
Mary	ЦНТ |||
Brent	ЦНТ ЦНТ |||
Dan	||

Which player scored the most goals? __Josh__
Which player scored only two goals? __Dan__
How many more goals did Brent score over Mary? __13 − 8 = 5__
Which two players scored as many goals together as Josh did by himself?
__Brent (13)__ and __Jane (3)__

55

Page 55